Enjoying the Library

Book B

Written by Jane Price

Published by Prim-Ed Publishing

Enjoying the Library
A Library Skills Programme for Primary Schools
Book B

The *Enjoying The Library* series comprises seven sequential packages, catering for all Year levels in the primary school. The packages are self-explanatory and have been designed for use in any library, regardless of the number of resources available to the pupils.

It should be stressed that the activities in the series are designed to be used by both classroom teachers and library specialists.

The series involves a thorough library programme. The emphasis is on 'hands-on' experience as this not only caters for individual abilities and differences but also gives pupils the opportunity to explore the resources available in the library.

The aim of this programme is to make students independent library users who can choose and use appropriate, relevant library resources. Specific reference to many parts of the shelves has been made to enable pupils to become familiar with the wide range of subjects offered.

Each package contains some forty activities lasting approximately thirty minutes each. This provides a complete year-long library study programme. However, in many schools a second period per week is also given. It is important that in the second session all pupils are given the opportunity to borrow resources. Lower primary pupils enjoy this time to be read a range of stories or be given the opportunity to complete any library work.

Suggestions for further research are given in the packages for the middle and upper primary Year levels. Appropriately, a research question relating to specific classroom activities should be given.

Contents

Enjoying the Library

Library Introduction

It is suggested that in their first lesson the students are introduced to the library.

Make them aware of:

- **the need for a library bag;**

- **the number of books they can borrow;**

- **the length of time they can borrow the books;**

- **how to return books; and**

- **the areas of the library, for example, games, books, magazines.**

To complete the lesson, read the children a story. They may also wish to borrow their first book.

Caring for Books

The following are suggestions to be used during the first two lessons, which should also be reinforced during the year.

Library books are precious as not only are they enjoyable resources, but they cost money, and other people will also want to read them.

Below are a few simple suggestions to make sure books are cared for.

1. **Use a library bag.**

2. **Keep your books out of the sun and damp places.**

3. **No tearing, scribbling or spilling food onto your books.**

4. **Always put your books in a safe place where you can find them.**

5. **Always have clean hands before you touch a book.**

Revision

Fill in the missing words.

1. _____ works in the library.

2. The day I have library skills is _____.

3. I must bring _____.

4. I can borrow _____ book(s).

5. I can borrow the book(s) for _____ weeks.

6. To protect my book, I need to put it in a

   _____.

Sample Borrower's Card
and Date Due Slip

Fill in the following cards. You must fill in one every time you take a book out.

Name of Author Title of Book		Call Number	
Book card, primary Borrower	Class	Date Due	
Simon Jones	2	12-4-99	

Sample Borrower's Card

Write your name and class number under 'Simon Jones'.

If your library has a computer you won't find a Borrower's Card in the books. Instead, you will need to tell the resource teacher your name.

Sample Date Due Slip

Include your class Year

12-4-99 (2)		

Browser Card

Name:

Cut out the browser card. Paste it onto a piece of cardboard.

WHEN TO USE IT
When looking at a book, put the card in its place so you know where to return the book.

Using your browser card, find a book to read.

Fiction Spine Label

Fiction books are shelved alphabetically according to the author's surname.

Fiction

First three letters of author's surname

F
Dan

Put these surnames into alphabetical order.

DODD   _____

CARLE   _____

ARNOLD   _____

FOX   _____

AHLBERG   _____

Write these spine labels in alphabetical order.

F	F	F	F	F
WIL	MAH	ADA	SCA	GOS

_____ _____ _____ _____ _____

Fiction

Use these words to answer the questions.

author   **fiction**   **title**

A _____ book is a storybook.

The _____ of a book is its name.

The _____ of a book is the person who wrote it.

Colour the book.

(Title)

(Author)

Parts of a Fiction Book

Colour in the cover.

The Clown

By P.O.P. Corn

Title

Author

Choose a fiction book.

Write down the:

Title: _____

Author: _____

Titles 1

Write down the titles of these books.

1.

FREDDO

By Nee Deep

2.

BEN'S TREE HOUSE

By Willie Climb-it

3.

THE LIGHTHOUSE MOUSE

By I. C. Dersea

4.

THOMAS THE TURTLE
By Iva Shell

1._____

2._____

_____

3._____

_____

4._____

Choose three fiction books.

Write down their titles.

1. _____

2. _____

3. _____

Draw one of the covers and write in the title.

Authors

Write down the authors of these books.

1.

FREDDO

By Nee Deep

2.

BEN'S TREE HOUSE

By Willie Climb-it

3.

THE LIGHTHOUSE MOUSE

By I. C. Dersea

4.

THOMAS THE TURTLE
By Iva Shell

1. _____

2. _____

3. _____

4. _____

Illustrator

What is an illustrator?_____

_____

Choose three books from the shelves.
Write down the author and illustrator.

1. Author: _____

    Illustrator: _____

2. Author: _____

    Illustrator: _____

3. Author: _____

    Illustrator: _____

Draw one of the covers. Write in the author's name and the illustrator's name.

(Author)_____

(Illustrator)_____

Using the 'Author' or 'Title' sheet, draw the following characters.

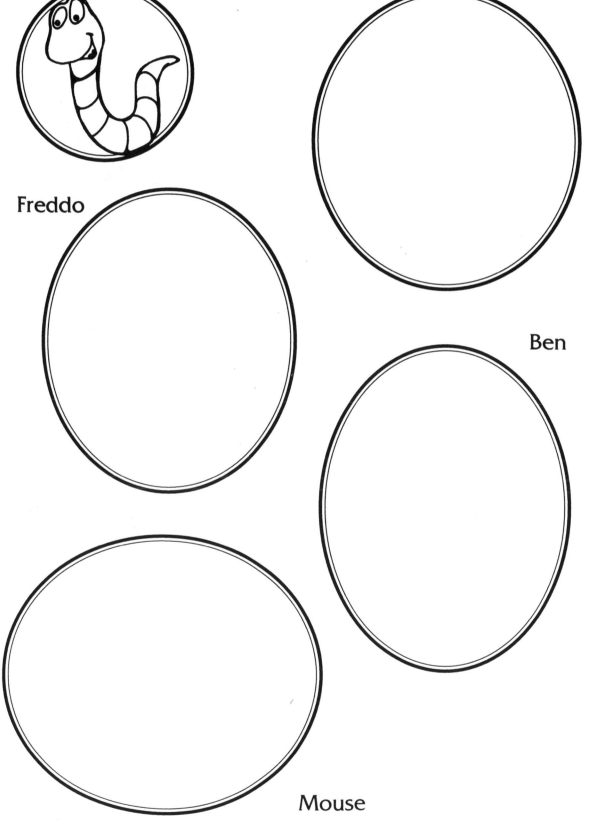

Thomas

Freddo

Ben

Mouse

Characters 2

Choose three fiction books.

Write the titles and draw a character from each.

_____
_____
_____

_____
_____
_____

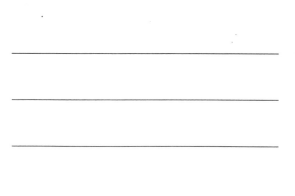

_____
_____
_____

Fiction Details 1

Look at the cover of the book below.

Write down the:

* Author:_____

* Title:_____

* Characters:_____

_____

Colour in the book.

Boy and Beatrice:

The Beautiful Birds

By
T. Weet

Fiction Details 2

Choose a fiction book to read.

Write down the:

* Author:_____

* Title:_____

* Characters:_____

Which character did you like the best and why?

_____

_____

Draw your favourite character in the book.

The Cover

Choose a fiction book.

Draw the cover below.

Read the book.

What do the title and cover tell you about the book?

_____

_____

_____

_____

Picture Books

Listen to a picture book being read to you.

What special things do picture books have?

_____

_____

_____

_____

Draw your favourite picture from your picture book.

Look through some picture books.

Name a picture book from your library.

_____

Fiction
Picture Books and Sequencing

You have just heard a story.
In the spaces below, draw what happened in the correct order.

1.	2.
3.	4.

Draw the things you need to listen to a story on tape.

T _____

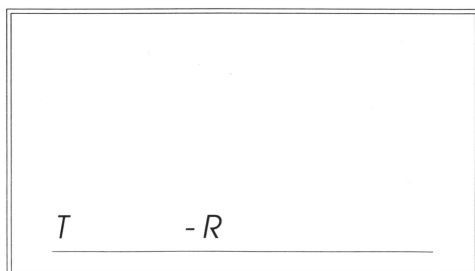

T _____ - R _____

Electric socket _____

Stories on Tape - Cover

If the story you listened to was made into a book, what cover would you like it to have?
What should you include on your cover?

_____

Design your own cover on the book below.

Non-fiction Spine Label

Non-fiction books are shelved according to their subject number.

808.8

WON

Subject number
(Dewey number)

First three letters of:
(a) author's surname;
or
(b) title of the book (when there is no author).

Write these spine labels in numerical order from lowest to highest.

237	512	707	238	354
BET	**HER**	**LAY**	**BET**	**DRA**

_____ _____ _____ _____ _____

Non-fiction

Use these words to answer the questions.

title   **author**   **non-fiction**

* A _____ book is a true book.

* The _____ of a book is its name.

* The _____ of a book is the person who wrote it.

Colour the cover of the book below. Give it a title and write your name where it says 'Author'.

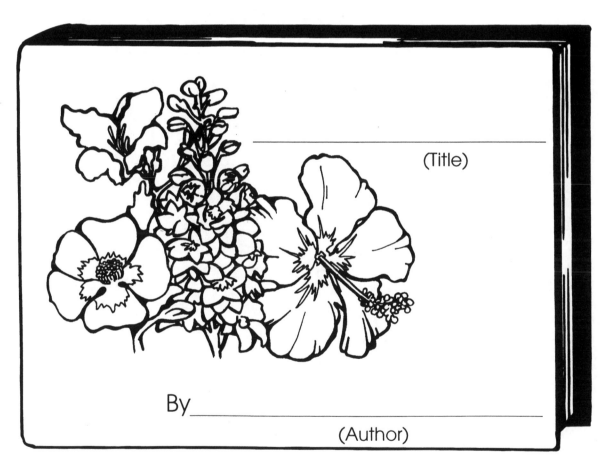

_____
(Title)

By_____
(Author)

What three letters would we find on the call number?

582
_____

Parts of a Non-fiction Book

Fill in the missing spaces.

INSECTS

By
D. Bug

T

A

Take a non-fiction book from the shelves.

Write down the:

Title: _____

Author: _____

Titles 1

Colour in the book below.

LEARNING THE PIANO

By C. A. Note

What is the title of the book?

_____

What three letters would we find on the spine label? _____

_____ Why? _____

_____

Titles 2

Choose a non-fiction book.

What is the title of the book?

_____

Design a new cover. Don't forget to include on your cover the title and author of the book.

Colour in the book below.

HOW TO PLAY
BASEBALL

WRITTEN BY E. C. SWING

What is the author's name?

_____

Below is a list of authors' surnames. What letters would you find on the spine labels?

Taylor	_____	Morris	_____
Smith	_____	Hansen	_____
Freed	_____	Ardley	_____

Authors 2

Choose 5 (five) non-fiction books which have the same Dewey decimal number. Write down the author and the spine label below.

Author   **Spine Label**

1. _____

2. _____

3. _____

4. _____

5. _____

Write the titles of the books in the order you would find them on the shelves. (As they all have the same Dewey decimal number, consider the first three letters of the author's surname.)

1. _____   2. _____

3. _____   4. _____

5. _____

Subjects 1

Look at the non-fiction shelves.

Non-fiction books are placed into groups.
These groups are called 'subjects'.

List some of the subjects you find.

_____

_____

_____

_____

_____

_____

_____

_____

_____

_____

Subjects 2

Your teacher will put three books on your desk.

Write down the following:

(1)
Author:_____

Title:_____

Subject:_____

(2)
Author:_____

Title:_____

Subject:_____

(3)
Author:_____

Title:_____

Subject:_____

Non-fiction Using Tapes

Listen carefully to a non-fiction audio tape.

Write down the following:

Author:_____

Title:_____

Call number:_____

What was the tape about?

_____

_____

_____

_____

_____

Did you find it easier to learn from a book or a tape?

_____

_____

Non-fiction Using Video 1

Show students a non-fiction video.

Discussion points for the teacher:
· Did students enjoy the video?
· Were they able to recall the major points?
· Do they prefer videos or books?
  Reasons why?

You are about to watch a non-fiction video.
Watch the video carefully.

Write down the title of the video.

_____

Design an attractive cover for the video.

Non-fiction Using Video 2

Watch the video carefully

What was the video about?

_____

_____

_____

_____

_____

_____

_____

_____

Non-fiction Using Charts

Healthy Foods

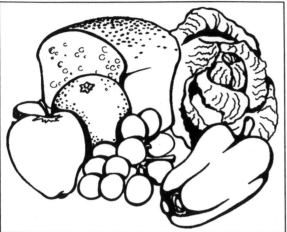

Unhealthy Foods

What is the chart trying to show?
List some points.

_____

_____

_____

List some of the foods shown in the chart.

Healthy Foods

_____

_____

_____

_____

Unhealthy Foods

_____

_____

_____

Fiction and Non-fiction Quiz

1. What is fiction? _____

_____

2. What is non-fiction? _____

_____

3. What does the author do? _____

_____

4. What is a title? _____

_____

5. Choose a fiction and a non-fiction book. Write the following details:

Fiction

    Author:_____

    Title:_____

    Spine label:_____

Non-fiction

    Author:_____

    Title:_____

    Spine label:_____

 # Sleuth

S	N	O	I	T	C	I	F	N	O	N	I	H	O
P	P	E	Y	O	U	E	N	J	P	O	P	Y	R
I	U	L	S	N	O	I	T	C	I	F	I	I	E
N	N	I	G	T	H	E	B	O	L	O	C	K	D
E	S	B	A	U	T	H	O	R	S	I	T	N	R
L	T	R	H	E	L	I	B	R	E	A	U	R	O
A	Y	A	T	H	E	Y	A	R	U	E	R	F	C
B	U	R	L	R	L	E	O	F	D	I	E	N	E
E	T	Y	E	E	R	L	E	S	E	T	B	I	R
L	N	G	I	V	N	T	F	O	T	R	O	M	E
A	U	D	I	O	V	I	S	U	A	L	O	A	P
R	T	I	O	C	N	T	F	O	D	R	K	Y	A
D	O	C	H	A	R	A	C	T	E	R	S	U	T

Find these words:

Audiovisual

Author

Spine label

Characters

Cover

Date due slip

Fiction

Library

Non-fiction

Picture books

Tape Recorder

Title